Critical Thinking
Problem Solving

Grades 5-6

Exploring Thinking

40001

by
Joy Hayes and
Marion M. Sebastian

 **JUDY/INSTRUCTO**   Minneapolis, MN 55406

Foreword

Thinking and problem solving are skills — basic skills, life skills, survival skills! Just like any other skills, they must be practiced if they are to be developed, depended upon, and useful. Playing tennis, swimming, cooking, driving an automobile, bicycling, and playing a musical instrument are skills. It is well known that they can be improved by coaching and practice. Thinking and problem solving, in a similar manner, require coaching and practice.

There has been much debate as to whether thinking and problem solving should be taught separately from the rest of the curriculum or as an integral part of the curriculum. My response is that, of course, problem solving and thinking skills should be taught separately from the rest of the curriculum. These skills cannot be used until they are mastered. It is frustrating to be given a problem in the curriculum for which a person does not have adequate skills. The focus is on curriculum, and the teaching of problem solving is likely to be forgotten. On the other hand, I would also say, "Of course, thinking and problem solving should be an integral part of every part of the curriculum — in language arts, reading, mathematics, geography, history, science, and so on." Thinking and problem solving are basic skills and should permeate all of the curriculum.

This is where <u>Problem of the Week</u> comes in. Its focus is on problem solving and thinking skills. Neither the pupil nor the teacher should have the burden of the curriculum on them. During the time the problem is being considered, some curricular objective in mathematics, history, or language arts may be mastered, but this is incidental. It is enough to master the problem-solving skill. When this is done, the skill can be used in any subject. Until the thinking and problem-solving skills are mastered, it is useless to think that they will be used in the curriculum or in life.

We do not know how often these skills should be practiced separately from the curriculum. Once a week is a good guess. It gives time for incubation to take place, and once a week is certainly not too frequent in my opinion.

E. Paul Torrance
Distinguished Professor/Emeritus/Founder, Future Problem Solving Center
University of Georgia
Athens, Georgia 30602

October 6, 1988

Table of Contents

Page

Foreword II

Review of Bloom's Taxonomy IV

Creative Problem Solving Skills IV

Suggested Procedure for use of this book . . . . V, VI

Problem of the week identified according to levels of Bloom's Taxonomy
   and Creative Problem Solving:

        Knowledge 16, 25

        Comprehension. 2

        Application 3, 4, 18, 27, 29

        Analysis 5, 7, 11, 12, 20, 26, 30, 31, 33, 34, 35

        Synthesis. 8, 15, 19, 23, 28, 36

        Evaluation 1, 9, 10, 13, 14, 21, 22, 32

        Creative Problem Solving 6, 17, 24

Holiday Bonus Problems:

        Halloween (synthesis). 37

        Winter (analysis) 38

        Valentine (evaluation) 39

Solution Slips for students' use. 40-50

Bulletin Board Model 51

Badges for Winners. 52

Answer Key 53-60

JI 2411 ©1989, Judy/Instructo, Minneapolis, MN 55406

A Brief Review of Bloom's Taxonomy

(A hierarchy of thinking skills based on *The Taxonomy of Educational Objectives: Handbook I: Cognitive Domain* by Benjamin S. Bloom, ©1956 by Longman Inc.)

Beginning at lowest level:

1. Knowledge: remembering previously learned material by gathering information, recalling, listing, and defining.

2. Comprehension: the ability to grasp the meaning of material by showing that you understand through interpreting, explaining, giving examples, and converting.

3. Application: using learned material in new and concrete situations by using the information to solve problems, constructing charts and graphs, modifying, and demonstrating.

4. Analysis: the ability to break down or see the parts of materials so that their organization may be understood. This involves breaking down, relating, distinguishing, and identifying.

5. Synthesis: putting parts together or forming a new whole by categorizing, compiling, relating, reorganizing, modifying, and creating.

6. Evaluation: judging the value of material for a given purpose by comparing, justifying, interpreting, supporting, and predicting.

Creative Problem Solving Skills

The steps and interpretations of Creative Problem-Solving Skills are many. The skills emphasized in the discussion of "Creative Problem Solving" solutions in this book are those learned by the authors from Dr. E. Paul and Mrs. Pansy Torrance. The Torrances taught the identification, encouragement, and assessment of these skills through their conference presentations, writings, and work with the Future Problem Solving Program. A more in-depth study of these skills and others for teaching creativity may be found in *The Search for Satori and Creativity* by E. Paul Torrance (published by Bearly Limited, 149 York St., Buffalo, New York 14213).

Skills emphasized in this book:

1. Fluency - generating a large number of ideas or alternative solutions to a problem.

2. Originality - giving a unique or unusual solution to a problem. The solution which no one else in class gives might be considered original.

3. Flexibility - seeing things from different points of view or viewing the problem in many different ways. A large number of categories of solutions shows flexibility.

4. Elaboration - expanding a basic idea by adding to it or building on it. A solution giving enough details to be understood clearly by the observer is elaborated.

The first Creative Problem Solution in this book explains more clearly how the teacher can help the students to understand and improve the skills listed above.

JI 2411 ©1989, Judy/Instructo, Minneapolis, MN 55406

Suggested Procedure for Use of This Book

1. Color and laminate the problem pages of this book to post in your "Problem of the Week" area.

2. Make enough copies of the student solution slips for the entire class plus a few extra copies. Cut them apart.

3. Create a center called "Problem of the Week" by posting the weekly problem and providing storage for solution slips and participation rules. The picture of the spaceship may be enlarged and posted in the center. Attach an envelope for completed solution slips on the spaceship.

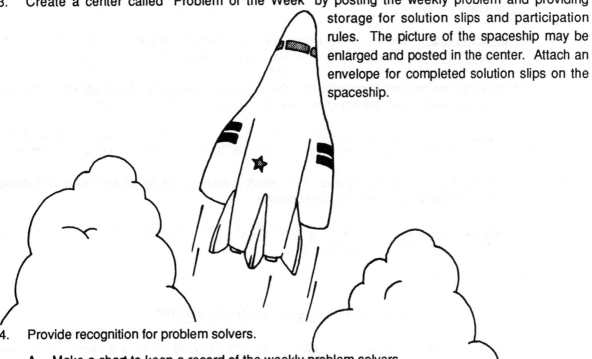

4. Provide recognition for problem solvers.

   A. Make a chart to keep a record of the weekly problem solvers.

   B. Recognition badges may be given to students who have correctly completed the solutions.

   C. The students may either wear their badges or display them in the center.

5. In presenting the "Problem of the Week," it is important to discuss some of these points at appropriate times.

   A. Different methods may be used to solve higher level thinking problems. Examples for grades five/six:

1. Make lists - week 15	5. Draw diagrams - week 34
2. Make tables - week 4	6. Guess and test - week 32
3. Draw pictures - week 3	7. Logic elimination - week 13
4. Identify patterns - week 5	8. Think of as many solutions as you can - week 6

Jl 2411 ©1989, Judy/Instructo, Minneapolis, MN 55406

B. There may be more than one way to get the correct solution to the problem. Some problems may have more than one solution. In creative problem solving, there are no specific, correct solutions.

6. Suggested rules for students at the center:

A. Allow students to work independently whenever they have spare time.

B. Students may choose to participate or not.

C. Completed solution slips must be returned to the center by the established deadline.

D. A student who has solved the problem should not tell anyone else the answer.

E. Solutions may be discussed at a certain time. All the possible ways to solve the problem should be demonstrated in order to help the students develop problem-solving techniques. Encourage the students to learn from one another during discussion.

7. You may want to set up a student corner so students can add problems they find or make up.

8. Use the special seasonal holiday puzzles as bonus problems or instead of other problems in the book.

9. A key ingredient to the success of this program is teacher enthusiasm in presenting the idea and in allowing time for enthusiastic discussion of the problem-solving methods used by the students each week to solve the problems.

JI 2411 ©1989, Judy/Instructo, Minneapolis, MN 55406

Problem of the Week

1

Jack, Edra, Julie, Terry, and Marie were excited that their families had decided to live in the first U.S. space colony, **Beyond.** They plan to travel to the colony in the same space shuttle. The seats are arranged so that one child will sit in each row, one in front of the other. Julie is in the last row.

Clue 1: Marie is sorry she can't sit in front of Terry so she can be first.

Clue 2: They all plan to read during the flights.

Clue 3: Julie borrows a book from Edra, and Miss Hayes sees Edra turn around.

Clue 4: There are only two people between Marie and Julie.

Clue 5: Julie cannot see Terry because all the children are in front of her.

Who sits up front?

Where do the others sit?

Evaluation

Problem of the Week

2

When the children become tired of reading, their teacher, Miss Hayes, shows them a cube that is blue only on the outside. The large cube has been cut into many smaller cubes.

1. How many cubes are there all together?

2. How many cubes have no blue sides?

3. How many cubes have only one blue side?

4. How many cubes have only two blue sides?

5. How many cubes have only three blue sides?

6. How many cubes have four blue sides?

Comprehension

Problem of the Week

3

As soon as the shuttle arrives at the landing port of the space colony, the children are eager to see their new homes. The families in the shuttle have to choose an arrangement for their living space. They are allowed four prefabricated rooms.

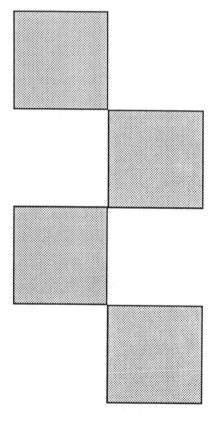

The perimeter of these prefabricated rooms is 80 meters. Each side equals 5 meters. The perimeter is the total of all the sides of the shaded squares. How can the families arrange their rooms to get the following perimeters?

1. 40 meters
2. 50 meters
3. 60 meters
4. 70 meters

Application

Problem of the Week

4

| 13 | 36 | 25 | 42 | 33 | 20 |

Each living space has a number just like house numbers. No one has chosen the following numbers yet: 13, 36, 25, 42, 33, 20. Edra asks Marie to guess which number her family will choose.

Clue 1: It is not a prime number.

Clue 2: The number has more than six factors.

Clue 3: The sum of the digits is a square number.

Can you help Marie guess the number?

Challenge: Select one of the other numbers. Write no more than three clues to help your classmates guess the number you selected.

Application

Problem of the Week

5

	Row 1	Row 2	Row 3	Row 4
	H	C	D	A
	I	S	P	V
	T	O		

Because of the limited room on the space shuttle, some household supplies are furnished for the space colony. Boxes of basic supplies are stacked for the new residents. Each box is coded with a letter from the alphabet.

Do you notice a pattern for the shapes of letters used in each vertical row of boxes? Write the missing letters to complete the horizontal rows.

Challenge: Explain the pattern.

Analysis

Problem of the Week

6

The Pulling family is among the new arrivals at the space colony. Mr. and Mrs. Pulling are both educators. They are very interested in meeting other new people to see what jobs they do. Many people are needed to do jobs to help the people live a normal life in the space colony.

List all the jobs which you think are necessary in a space colony.

Creative Problem Solving

Problem of the Week

7

Each area of the colony has a medical unit. Use these clues to answer some questions about the medical unit.

Clue 1: In the medical unit, there are half as many lab technicians as there are nurses.

Clue 2: There are exactly half as many doctors as there are x-ray technicians.

Clue 3: There are three times as many lab technicians as there are doctors.

Clue 4: The total number of jobs, including lab technicians, nurses, doctors, and x-ray technicians, equals 12.

1. How many lab technicians are there?

2. How many nurses are there?

3. How many doctors are there?

4. How many x-ray technicians are there?

Challenge: If the total number of jobs equals 36, how many lab technicians, nurses, doctors, and x-ray technicians are there? Use clues 1, 2, and 3 to solve the challenge.

Analysis

Problem of the Week

8

Many of the physical activities that are popular on earth are not possible in the same way in the colony, due to the limited space and physical makeup of the colony. Each area of the colony has a gymnasium that is the size of a football field. How would you design that area to provide a variety of physical activities for both adults and children? You may draw and label the part of the gymnasium, or you may describe the area in a paragraph.

Synthesis

Problem of the Week

9

This space colony is constantly rotating. The designers of the colony found they could not use the standard map directions of north, south, east, and west as reference points. People need some form of map key in order to give directions or find locations. What type of map would you develop for the colony? You should be able to convince the class that your system will work. Your system should be easy to remember and use. The points of reference should be the same.

Evaluation

Name _____

Problem of the Week

vermilion	magenta
emerald	indigo

The designers of the space colony decide that this first colony, **Beyond,** would use colors as the points of reference for maps of the colony. The colors chosen are magenta, indigo, emerald, and vermilion. Four families have the same last names as those four colors. None of those families lives in the area that has the same color as their name.

Clue 1: The Indigo family does not live in the indigo section.

Clue 2: The Indigo family also does not live on the emerald side or the vermilion side.

Clue 3: The Vermilion family does not live in the indigo section.

Clue 4: The Emerald family lives to the right of the Vermilion family, while the Vermilion family lives opposite the Indigo family.

Challenge: Define and find examples of each of the four colors.

Evaluation

11

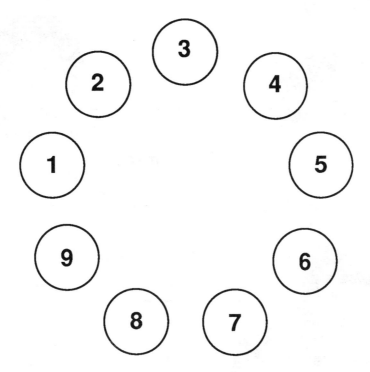

On the first day of the new school session, Mrs. DeNote's math class plays a new game. The children sit in a circle. Each chair in the circle has a number. Here are the rules for the math game:

1. Player 1 starts by asking the player on the left a math problem. That student (number 2) must leave the circle to work the problem on the class visual board. The next player continues the game immediately and so on around the circle.

2. Once you leave the circle, you cannot return until the next game. The second round of the game continues, just like the first one, using the players still at their seats.

Marie doesn't like working problems on the board. Where should she sit to avoid going to the board at all during this game?

Analysis

Problem of the Week

12

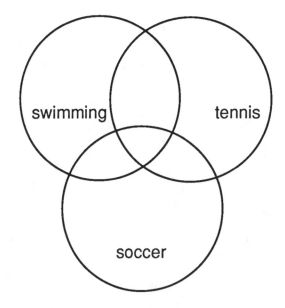

As the students in Mrs. DeNote's class become better acquainted, they discover that many of them enjoy the same sports.

Eleven students enjoy swimming.

Nine students enjoy tennis.

Seven students enjoy soccer.

Three enjoy both tennis and swimming but not soccer.

One enjoys tennis and soccer but not swimming.

Two enjoy all three sports.

How many students are in Mrs. DeNote's class? You should be able to use the circles and numbers to help you find the answer.

Analysis

Problem of the Week

13

The space colony **Beyond** is having its first swim meet. Students from each of four areas come for the competition. The students representing the vermillion area are from six different classrooms. While waiting for the diving competition to finish, the students from the school in the emerald area try to guess which student came from which room. Use the clues and the grid to see if you can decide. The first clue is marked on the grid for you.

Clue 1: Tommy's class is in an end room.

Clue 2: Mark and Susie McQueen have teachers with the same first name.

Clue 3: Dr. Belden's room has a red sign on the door.

Clue 4: The same numeral appears twice on the door to Nicki's room.

Clue 5: Mrs. Berrong teaches next to the room Carla is in.

Clue 6: Susie is not in the room with the red sign on the door.

	142 Mr. George Thompson	143 Dr. Edith Belden	144 Mrs. Ruth Cowen	145 Mrs. Edith Chapman	146 Mrs. Jerri Berrong	147 Dr. Lowell Ensey
Tommy		X	X	X	X	
Carla						
Susie						
Mark						
Greg						
Nicki						

Evaluation

Problem of the Week

14

News is a vital part of life in the space colony, **Beyond.** The news agency reports all the news to the citizens of the colony. Use the clues and grid below to determine each person's job in the agency.

Clue 1: Mr. Trapani is taller than the head technician or business manager.
Clue 2: The editor eats lunch alone in the office.
Clue 3: Ms. Moody jogs with Mrs. McQueen.
Clue 4: The tallest of the four plays basketball.
Clue 5: Mr. Lee lunches with the head technician and the business manager.
Clue 6: Mrs. McQueen is older than the head technician.
Clue 7: Mr. Trapani plays no sports.

	Editor	Reporter	Business Manager	Head Technician
Mrs. McQueen				
Mr. Trapani				
Ms. Moody				
Mr. Lee				

Evaluation

Problem of the Week

15

space colony

News is very slow some days at the news agency. One of the computer technicians decides to see how many words she can make from the words, space colony. How many words can you find using only the letters from the words below?

space colony

Challenge: Alphabetize your list of words.

Synthesis

Problem of the Week

16

People at the news agency are very word conscious. They need to use as few words as possible to describe important news accurately. Identify the parts of speech for the words below as either an adjective, adverb, noun, or verb.

1. orbital
2. yesterday
3. insulate
4. scrutinize
5. reuseable

6. high-speed
7. flights
8. quickly
9. payload
10. tomorrow

11. accelerate
12. flew
13. astronaut
14. technology
15. carefully

Challenge: Can you use all of the words above in just two or three sentences that make sense?

Knowledge

Problem of the Week

Homework

List the different ways you can find to use a large garbage bag!

Storage and disposal space is very limited on **Beyond.** People must learn to make the most efficient use of all their materials. Sometimes in the ecology class, the children discuss ways to recycle materials. One of the homework assignments is to think of all the ways people can use and reuse a large plastic garbage bag. List the different ways you can use a large plastic garbage bag.

Creative Problem Solving

Problem of the Week _____

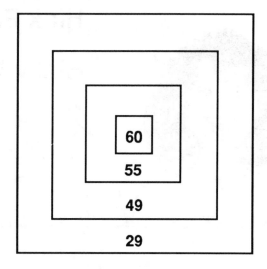

Mrs. DeNote's math class enjoys making games for other grade levels. Jack has a game to help third graders practice adding. Each student tosses a disk five times at the target above. Find the sum of the numbers in the areas where the disk lands.

Each child's total is shown below on the chart. Use the totals to figure out where each disk landed. You do not need to get the tosses in the correct order.

						Total
Example	60	29	49	60	29	227
Amanda		60				248
Christopher			55			273
Karon				29		227
JoDee	49					253

Application

— Problem of the Week —

19

Hink Pinks

Hinky Pinkies

Hink pinks are one-syllable rhyming words that fit a definition.

Example: heavenly secret agent = sky spy

Hinky pinkies are two-syllable rhyming words that fit a definition.

Example: to improve space = enhance expanse

During the language lesson, Mrs. Pulling's class worked on definitions of words. Terry thought of a good hink pink to go with one of the definitions. Mrs. Pulling asked the students to write more hink pinks to go with the other definitions.

How many hink pinks and hinky pinkies can you solve? They all relate to space.

Hink Pinks

1. Sun's rays warm the spaceship.

2. Appearance of **Discover** on radar.

3. Smooth sailing of **Beyond** in orbit.

4. Sun's appearance from Earth and **Beyond.**

Hinky Pinkies

1. Light fixture in propulsion area.

2. Hard, rock-like appearance of Venus from **Beyond.**

Challenge: Can you make up some more hink pinks and hinky pinkies?

Synthesis

Problem of the Week

20

Terry's class is learning to use the almanac. Terry finds that it is not always easy to use the index of the almanac, but with persistence, he is able to complete the following analogies. For example, foot is to shoe as hand is to glove. Now complete the analogies below.

1. Moon is to Earth as Titan is to _____.

2. Vostok 1 is to Yuri Gagarin as Mercury Redstone 3 is to _____.

3. Pisces is to fishes as Taurus is to _____.

4. Telescope is to Hans Lippershay as laser is to _____.

Challenge: Create some more analogies for the class to solve. Be sure to give the teacher your correct answer.

Analysis

Problem of the Week

21

Julie's class wants to start a magazine. To test the popularity of the magazine, the students send copies to some of the residents of **Beyond.** Figure out how Julie's class decides who will receive copies of the magazine.

These people, named below, receive the magazine.

J. Greenway

B. Prince

P. Drake

K. Trapani

These people, named below, do not receive the magazine.

H. Cox

A. Allen

J. Jewett

M. Espada

Which of these people receive the magazine?

M. Krane

B. Franks

L. Thomas

D. Calvert

Evaluation

Problem of the Week

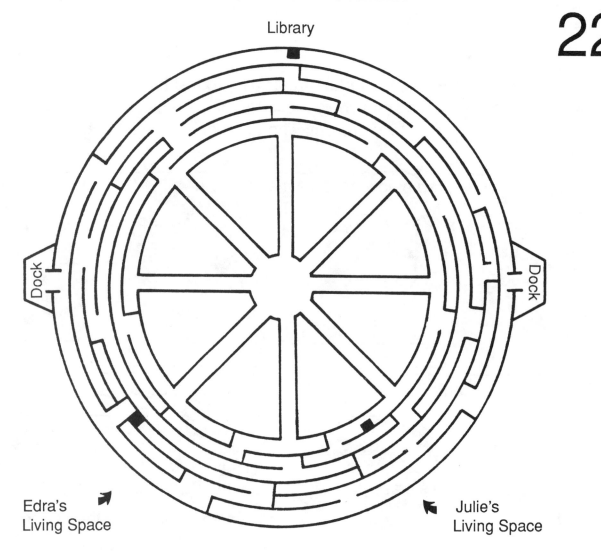

Library

Dock

Dock

Edra's
Living Space

Julie's
Living Space

Edra and her friend on Earth, Sarah, liked to send each other problems to solve. Edra sent Sarah a maze of the spaceship corridors. She asked Sarah to draw the shortest route from Edra's living space to the library. Then she wanted Sarah to find the shortest route to the library from Julie's living space. Which girl has the shortest route to the library?

Evaluation

Problem of the Week

23

Sarah enjoyed the maze Edra sent her. Sarah sent Edra the following rebus. Figure out the message for Edra.

L + (GIVE - G -E) + ( )- R   - P

SP + (- F)   M + (- B) + T

- E   F +(-S)

Challenge: Create a message in a rebus for the class to figure out.

Synthesis

Problem of the Week

24

Julie and her brother were waiting for their father to return from Earth on a spaceship. They talked about why it was called a ship. Julie asked her brother to name all the ways the word ship can be used.

How many ships can you name?

Creative Problem Solving

Problem of the Week

25

Marie's family likes to play a space trivia game. She decides to become an expert in one area of space knowledge. She made two lists of related space information so she could remember the facts better. Correctly match the items on the two lists below:

List 1
Comet
Planet
Asteroid
Moon
Star
Galaxy
Constellation

List 2
Pluto
Sun
Miranda
Ursa Major
Milky Way
Halley
Ceres

Challenge: Can you research one more example of each of the categories in List 1?

Knowledge

Problem of the Week

Dear Edra,

My dog family house garage will went help wants come tell think see observe to by at for with of live repair answer listen rake cut fold on by at for with of beside in Beyond Earth Mars Sun Venus Atlanta Pluto Boston star soon!

Sarah

Edra just received a letter from her friend, Sarah, on Earth. She wrote that she had important news, and she put it in code. Sarah gave only two clues: the first word in the first line is the first word of the message, and the message is a total of eight words. Decode Sarah's important news for Edra.

Analysis

Problem of the Week

27

Jack has a special talent. He can look at objects in his mind and visualize how they fit together. Look at the shapes below. Draw all the pieces together to form a square.

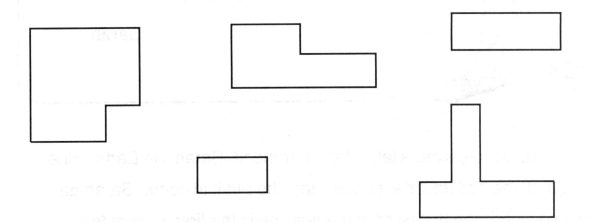

Challenge: Use all the pieces to make other interesting shapes. Does your shape resemble anything familiar?

Application

Problem of the Week

28

Sarah's first day of school at the space colony was a real surprise. Modern technology was used in her classroom.

What do you think Sarah's classroom looked like? Draw and label each area in the new classroom and describe its use. Be sure the area in the classroom is used efficiently. Think **future**!

Synthesis

Name _____

29

Learning to think and see things in new ways is an important part of the school program on **Beyond.** Mrs. Pulling's fifth grade class enjoys figuring out puzzles. Look at the puzzle below to figure out the words or phrases.

1.   2.

E
C
N
I
A
P
S

PRO   GRAM

3.   4.

I N G
ORBIT

SUN
● ● ●
● ● ●
● ●

5.   6.

S P A C E

WEIGHT
— NESS

Challenge: Create a few word puzzles of your own.

Application

Problem of the Week

The students in Mrs. Pulling's class use their calculators to play games. One of their favorite games is Missing Digit Caper, a game for using clues to discover the missing digits. See how well you can play Missing Digit Caper to find the missing digits below.

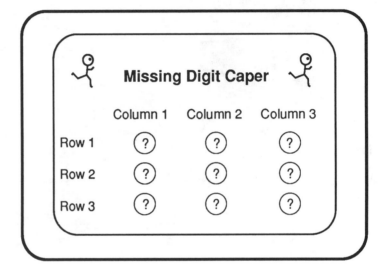

Missing Digit Caper

	Column 1	Column 2	Column 3
Row 1	?	?	?
Row 2	?	?	?
Row 3	?	?	?

Clue 1: All numbers are one digit from 1 to 9.

Clue 2: No number is used twice.

Clue 3: Row 1 has all even numbers in consecutive order.

Clue 4: The sum of the four corners equals the sum of each diagonal.

Clue 5: Row 2 has all odd numbers. The largest and smallest numbers are included.

Clue 6: The sum of column 3 is equal to three times the sum of column 1.

Clue 7: The numbers in row 1 are all factors of 12.

Clue 8: The sum of row 3 is equal to the sum of column 3.

Clue 9: The sum of each diagonal is equal to the sum of column 3.

Clue 10: The numbers in columns 1 and 3 are consecutive counting numbers but are not arranged in counting order.

Analysis

Name _____

Problem of the Week

31

One computer game the students like to play is called Space Hangman. They have to select the word that does not belong with the others. If they choose the wrong word, part of the hangman appears. See how well you do at the game.

1. Houston   Huntsville   Cape Canaveral   Chicago
2. Solar   Electrode   Wind   Thermal   Water
3. Gemini   Apollo   Soyuz   Skylab   Mercury
4. John Glenn   Neil Armstrong   Richard E. Byrd   Charles Conrad
5. Challenger   Discovery   Eagle   Atlantis   Columbia

Challenge: Label each category above.

Analysis

Problem of the Week

32

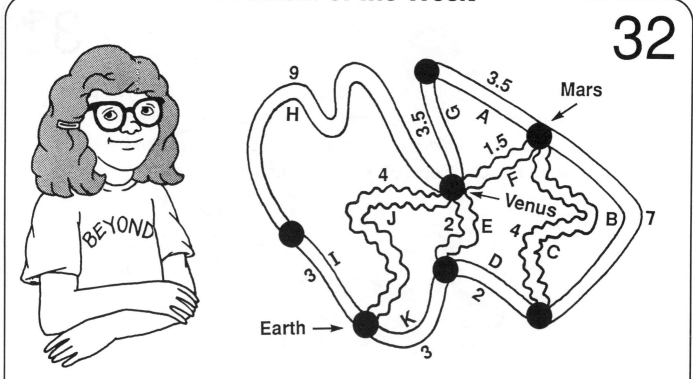

The racing club is one of the most popular clubs for children on **Beyond**. The members build and race remote control cars. Julie designed the course for the next race.

The longer routes are faster, making it easier to control the cars. The shorter, bumpy routes require more time and involve greater risk. All cars must begin at checkpoint Mars, must cross checkpoint Venus, and finish at checkpoint Earth.

Julie calculated that it takes the same amount of time to go 4 meters on the smooth road as it does to go 1 meter on the bumpy road. Which route would you follow to finish in the fastest possible time? List, in order, the letters for each segment you would take.

Challenge: Which route would take the longest time?

Evaluation

Name _____

Problem of the Week

33

Another popular club is the Astronauts of Tomorrow club. The club members learn skills to be good astronauts. One of those skills is the ability to recognize objects from different viewpoints. Look at the following side views to pick out each object as it would be seen from above.

1.

2.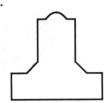

3.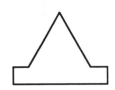

4.

5.

6.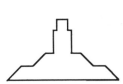

7.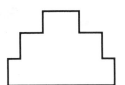

8.

A.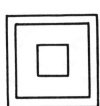

B.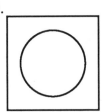

C.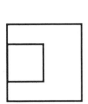

D.

E.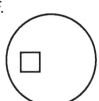

F.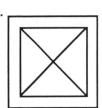

G.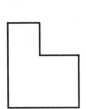

H.

Analysis

JI 2411 ©1989, Judy/Instructo, Minneapolis, MN 55406

Problem of the Week

34

The club members like to solve word puzzles. Can you solve this puzzle?

All astronauts are pilots.

None of my relatives is an astronaut.

Some of my relatives are men.

Which one of the statements below must be true?

1. Astronauts who are men are relatives of mine.

2. None of my relatives are pilots.

3. Some men are not astronauts.

Analysis

Problem of the Week

FAIRBURN PRINTER

Mrs. Humphries sent this word problem about a family on Earth to the club for a solution.

Some members of the Cox family work at the Fairburn Printers.

All work for the Fairburn Printers is done at their store in Fairburn, Georgia.

None of the Cox family lives in Fairburn, Georgia.

Which one of the statements must be true?

1. All members of the Cox family work in Fairburn, Georgia.

2. Some members of the Cox family do not work at Fairburn Printers.

3. No one who works at Fairburn Printers lives in Fairburn.

Challenge: Can you write some more true statements based on the information you are given in the problem?

Analysis

Problem of the Week

The children knew when they returned to Earth that they would be asked to describe their year in the space colony **Beyond.** Pretend you are one of these children. Write a well-organized speech which tells about life on **Beyond.**

Challenge: What kinds of visual aids would you use to make your speech more interesting?

Synthesis

Problem of the Week

Halloween costumes are not part of the standard equipment which could be taken to **Beyond.** Design a costume using some of these things usually found in each family's living space. Be creative. Tell what your costume represents.

Items: Regular clothes   Paper plates and cups

Old sheets and rags   Plastic dinner and cookware

Boxes   Plastic bags

Paper bags   Yarn and ribbons

Equipment to use in the space colony

Synthesis   **HOLIDAY BONUS #1**

Problem of the Week

In December, Mrs. Pulling's class was studying holiday customs on Earth. The logic puzzle below tells about one custom. See how the columns are numbered. Compare column 1 to column 2. Repeat the pattern for column 3. Choose a letter from column A, B, C, or D which corresponds to column 3.

1	2	3	A	B	C	D
G	G	S	S	S	S	S
I	i	W	W	M	W	W
F	F	A	A	▷	A	A
T	T	P	℧	P	P	℧

Now write the letters in columns 1 and 3 to tell about a holiday custom on Earth.

Problem of the Week

Mrs. DeNote's class decides to make their own valentines. They decide to make them in the shape of spacecrafts using only the shapes of hearts. Can you design a spacecraft using only hearts?

Have a contest in your room. Choose the winners in the following categories:

funniest spacecraft

prettiest spacecraft

spacecraft with the most details

spacecraft most likely to fly

Evaluation   **HOLIDAY BONUS #3**

Name _____ **Problem #1**

Turn this slip sideways to list how the children were seated.

Front

Miss Hayes

Name _____ **Problem #2**

1. _____ cubes all together.
2. _____ cubes have no blue sides.
3. _____ cubes have only one blue side.
4. _____ cubes have only two blue sides.
5. _____ cubes have only three blue sides.
6. _____ cubes have four blue sides.

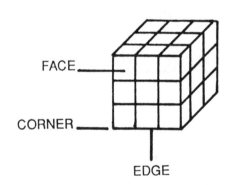

FACE

CORNER

EDGE

Name _____ **Problem #3**

Draw an arrangement to fit each perimeter.

1. 40 meters   2. 50 meters   3. 60 meters   4. 70 meters

Name _____ **Problem #4**

20

33

Edra's family chose number _____.

13

Challenge: Write the number you selected here _____.
Write your clues to the class on the back of this slip.

25

36   42

Name _____ **Problem #5**

Fill in the letters that would fit the existing pattern.

Challenge: Explain the pattern.

Row 1	Row 2	Row 3	Row 4
H	C	D	A
I	S	P	V
T	O		

Name _____ **Problem #7**

1. There are _____ lab technicians.
2. There are _____ nurses.
3. There are _____ doctors.
4. There are _____ x-ray technicians.

Write the **Challenge** on the back.

Name _____ **Problem #9**

Label the points of reference on the ship. Be able to convince the class your system will work.

Name _____ **Problem #10**

On the blank near each area, write the name of the family who lives there.

Write the **Challenge** on the back.

_____

_____

vermilion	magenta
emerald	indigo

_____

_____

Name _____ **Problem #11**

Marie should sit in chair _____ to avoid going to the board at all during the game.

2 3 4
1   5
9   6
8 7

Cut apart for student solution slips.

Name _____ **Problem #12**

Fill in the numbers in the circles from the information given in the problem. Then determine how many students are in Mrs. DeNote's class.

Total students = _____

Name _____ **Problem #13**

Tommy is in room # _____.
Carla is in room # _____.
Susie is in room # _____.
Mark is in room # _____.
Greg is in room # _____.
Nicki is in room # _____.

	142 Mr. George Thompson	143 Dr. Edith Belden	144 Mrs. Ruth Cowen	145 Mrs. Edith Chapman	146 Mrs. Jeri Berrong	147 Dr. Lowell Ensey
Tommy		X	X	X	X	
Carla						
Susie						
Mark						
Greg						
Nicki						

Name _____ **Problem #14**

Mrs. McQueen is the _____.
Mr. Trapani is the _____.
Ms. Moody is the _____.
Mr. Lee is the _____.

	Editor	Reporter	Business Manager	Head Technician
Mrs. McQueen				
Mr. Trapani				
Ms. Moody				
Mr. Lee				

Name _____   **Problem #16**

Write the code for the part of speech: adj = adjective   adv = adverb
                                            n = noun   v = verb

1. orbital _____   6. high-speed _____   11. accelerate _____
2. yesterday _____   7. flights _____   12. flew _____
3. insulate _____   8. quickly _____   13. astronaut _____
4. scrutinize _____   9. payload _____   14. technology _____
5. reuseable _____   10. tomorrow _____   15. carefully _____

Write the **Challenge** on the back.

Name _____   **Problem #18**

Fill in the numbers for each student.

Amanda   = _____, _____, _____, _____ + 60 = 248

Christopher   = _____, _____, _____, _____ + 55 = 273

Karon   = _____, _____, _____, _____ + 29 = 227

JoDee   = _____, _____, _____, _____ + 49 = 253

Name _____   **Problem #19**

The hink pinks are: The hinky pinkies are:
1. _____   1. _____
2. _____   _____
3. _____   2. _____
4. _____   _____

Write the **Challenge** on the back.

Cut apart for student solution slips.

Name _____ **Problem #20**

1. Moon is to Earth as Titan is to _____.
2. Vostok I is to Yuri Gagarin as Mercury Redstone 3 is to _____.
3. Pisces is to fishes as Taurus is to _____.
4. Telescope is to Hans Lippershay as laser is to _____.

Write the **Challenge** on the back.

Name _____ **Problem #21**

Which ones in the bottom row receive the magazine?

The people who receive the magazine are: _____ and

_____

because _____

_____

Name _____ **Problem #23**

L + (GIVE - G -E) + (🔥)- R 🔍 - P

SP + (😊 - F)   M + (🚌 - B) + T

🪰 - E   F +(☀ -S)

The message is: _____

Challenge: Write your rebus on the back or on a separate sheet of paper.

Cut apart for student solution slips.

Name ________________________________ **Problem #22**

Library
Dock
Dock
Edra's
Living Space
Julie's
Living Space

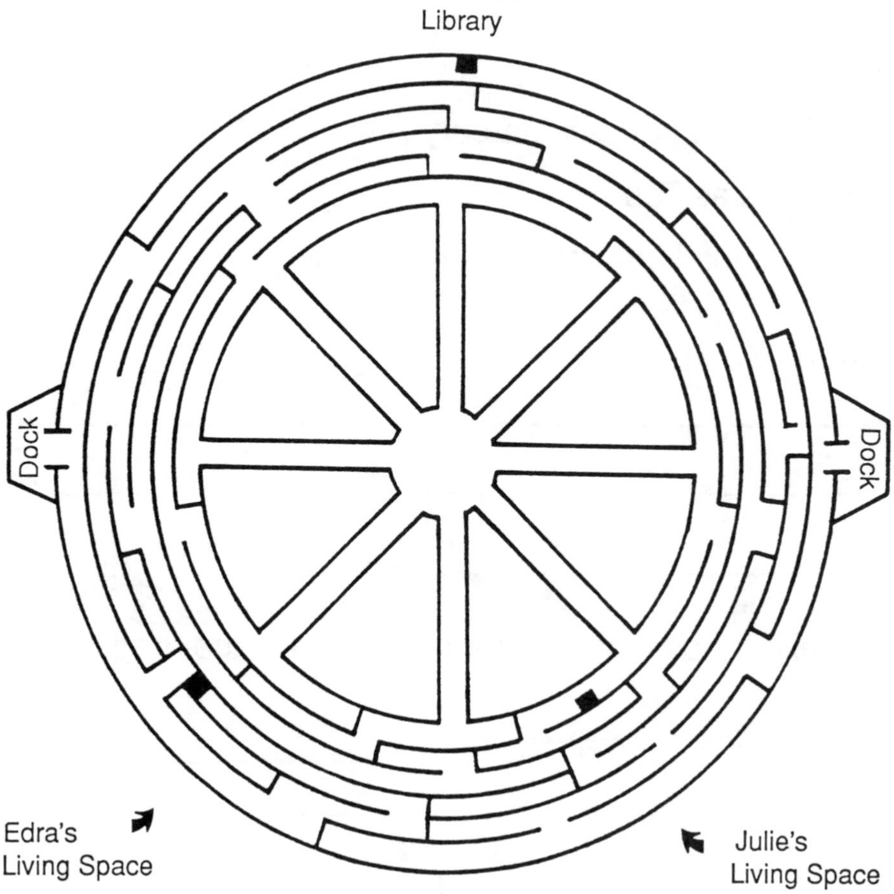

________________________ has the shortest route from the library.

Name ________________________________ **Problem #25**

Write the correct answer beside each term:

List 1	**List 2**	**Challenge**
1. Comet	____________	____________
2. Planet	____________	____________
3. Asteroid	____________	____________
4. Moon	____________	____________
5. Star	____________	____________
6. Galaxy	____________	____________
7. Constellation	____________	____________

Name _____ **Problem #26**

Circle the words in the letter that make up the message.

(My) dog family house garage will went help wants come tell think see observe to by at for with of live repair answer listen rake cut fold on by at for with of beside in Beyond Earth Mars Sun Venus Atlanta Pluto Boston star soon!

Name _____ **Problem #27**

Sketch how the five big pieces fit together to form a square.

Draw the **Challenge** on the back.

Name _____ **Problem #29**

1. _____ 4. _____
2. _____ 5. _____
3. _____ 6. _____

Write the **Challenge** on the back.

Cut apart for student solution slips.

Name _____ **Problem #30**

	Column 1	Column 2	Column 3
Row 1	◯	◯	◯
Row 2	◯	◯	◯
Row 3	◯	◯	◯

Name _____ **Problem #31**

Write the word that does not belong: **Challenge**: Label each category.

1. _____   1. _____
2. _____   2. _____
3. _____   3. _____
4. _____   4. _____
5. _____   5. _____

Name _____ **Problem #32**

The letter order for the route for the shortest time is:

_____

Challenge: The route for the longest time is:

_____

JI 2411 ©1989, Judy/Instructo, Minneapolis, MN 55406

Name _____ **Problem #33**

Match the letter of the overhead view with its side view.

1. _____   4. _____   7. _____

2. _____   5. _____   8. _____

3. _____   6. _____

Name _____ **Problem #34**

Circle the statement that must be true.

1. Astronauts who are men are relatives of mine.

2. None of my relatives are pilots.

3. Some men are not astronauts.

Name _____ **Problem #35**

Circle the statement that must be true.

1. All members of the Cox family work in Fairburn, Georgia.

2. Some members of the Cox family do not work at Fairburn Printers.

3. No one who works at Fairburn Printers lives in Fairburn.

Challenge: Write other true statements on the back.

Name _____   **Bonus Week #2**

Column 1 is to column 2 as column 3 is to which column?
Place the column letter for the correct answer beside the letter from column 3.

S _____   W _____   A _____   P _____

The holiday custom on Earth which is spelled in columns 1 and 3 is

_____

Bonus Week #3

HEART PATTERNS

Can You Solve the

Problem of the Week?

JI 2411 ©1989, Judy/Instructo, Minneapolis, MN 55406

I LOVE A CHALLENGE!

FINDING ANSWERS IS OUT OF THIS WORLD!

I CAN THINK BEYOND!

EXPLORING IS GREAT!

I'M AN EXPLORER TOO!

I REACHED BEYOND.

I Found the Answer.

Answer Key

Problem 1: The order is Terry in front, then Marie, Jack, Edra, Julie.

Clue 1	Clue 2	Clue 3	Clue 4	Clue 5
Terry	irrelevant	Terry	Terry	Terry
Marie		Marie	Marie	Marie
		Edra	_?_	Jack
		Julie	Edra	Edra
			Julie	Julie

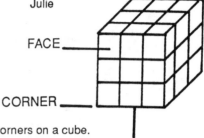

FACE

CORNER

EDGE

Problem 2:
1. <u>28</u> cubes (3 X 3 X 3 + 1); W X D X H + 1 original cube.
2. <u>1</u> has no blue sides (only the one in the very center).
3. <u>6</u> cubes have only one blue side. There are 6 faces to a cube. The center cube of each outside face is blue.
4. <u>12</u> cubes have only 2 blue sides, the middle of each edge. There are 12 edges to a cube.
5. <u>8</u> cubes have only 3 blue sides, each of the corners. There are 8 corners on a cube.
6. <u>0</u> cubes have 4 blue sides.

Problem 3: Each side equals 5 meters. To find the perimeter, use 2L + 2W or 2 (L + W). There are several possible answers for each perimeter. Accept any that are correct. Below are some possibilities.

1. 40 meters

2. 50 meters

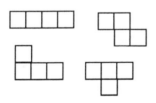

3. 60 meters

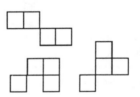

4. 70 meters

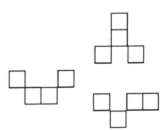

Problem 4: Edra's family chose number <u>36</u>.
Clue 1: Eliminates 13: 13 X 1.
Clue 2: Eliminates 25: factors are 5 X 5, 25 X 1.
Eliminates 33: factors are 33 X 1, 11 X 3.
Eliminates 20: factors are 5 X 4, 20 X 1, 2 X 10.
It does not eliminate 36 and 42 since:
36 = 6 X 6, 2 X 18, 9 X 4, 12 X 3, 36 X 1
42 = 21 X 2, 42 X 1, 7 X 6, 3 X 14
Clue 3: 36 = 3 + 6 = 9; 9 is a square number, 3^2 or 3 X 3 = 9.
42 = 4 + 2 = 6 which is not a square number.

Challenge: Possible clues students might use for other numbers:
25 - odd number, has at least 4 factors, 5 is a factor, is a square number, sum of its digits is a prime number.

42 - even number, 6 is a factor (others are 2, 21, 7, 3, 14), highest number in the group.

13 - odd number, prime number, sum of its digits is an even number.

33 - odd number, 3 is a factor (other factors are 11, 1, 33), only has four factors, sum of its digits is twice the first (or last) digit.

20 - even number, 10 is a factor (others are 4, 5, 2, 20, 1), sum of its digits equals its first digit, multiple of 5 (or 10).

Problem 5: The pattern for each row is:

Row 1- any letter with straight lines : F, E, L.

Row 2 - any letter with curved lines: Q, U.

Row 3 - any letter with straight lines and curved lines: B, J, G, R, U.

Row 4 - any letter with diagonal or angular lines: K, Y, M, N, W, X, Z.

Problem 6: There is no solution slip provided since we do not want to limit a child's thinking due to lack of writing space. The students may use as many sheets of notebook paper as needed to record solutions.

Warm-up: To get the students accustomed to thinking of many solutions, you may wish to have them, as a class, brainstorm all kinds of machines there might be in the space colony. You should encourage students to take turns saying anything that comes to mind. In brainstorming, all answers are accepted; no judgment is made at this time; students may add to or change a solution someone else mentioned; and even wild and "far out" solutions are encouraged and accepted. Be sure to accept solutions of machines which might be needed in the future, even if we do not have them now.

Discussion and Procedure to Emphasize Skills in Discussing Solutions:

Tell the students to number the jobs they wrote. Ask how many each person named as being necessary in the space colony, or to keep from embarrassing those who thought of few jobs, ask those who had over 10 jobs to raise their hands, over 15, etc., until there are so few hands, you can ask them to give the exact number.

Ask the person with the most different jobs to read his/her list aloud to the class. The person with the most different jobs will get special recognition as the "fluency" winner. You may want to explain that fluency means being able to give a lot of answers.

While the "fluency" winner reads his/her list, ask the others to check their answers to see if they thought of jobs the winner did not name. Have those students read those different answers. If a student (or students) has a solution which no one else thought of, declare that (those) student(s) winner of a special "originality" award. (Perhaps it could be a teacher-made ribbon, certificate, or badge with a special color or mark on it.) Help emphasize that having a mind-set of thinking of jobs just needed here on Earth usually does not produce original answers.

Next have the students categorize their solutions. (You may want to use the 15 career clusters designated by the U.S. Office of Education listed below.) The person with the most categories can be recognized as the "flexibility" winner. The class could listen to several students read their lists aloud to help choose ways to categorize the jobs so they all understand the step.

The 15 categories with possible answers for each are:
1. Agri-Business and Natural Resources: farmers, food handlers, air purification technicians
2. Business and Office: secretaries, clerks, managers
3. Communication and Media: television workers, telephone technicians
4. Construction: colony repair workers, new construction workers
5. Environment: heating and cooling technicians
6. Consumer and Homemaking: maids, store employees
7. Fine Arts and Humanities: artists, musicians
8. Health Services: doctors, nurses, nurses' aids, orderlies
9. Hospitality, Recreation, Leisure: park directors, welcome station attendants
10. Manufacturing: (only those types deemed practical in the colony)
11. Marine Science: (only if live sea creatures are in the colony for food or educational purposes)
12. Marketing and Distribution: for supplies to be sold in the colony
13. Personal Services: beauticians, barbers

14. Public Services: elected or appointed officials, charity organizers
15. Transportation: moving sidewalk operators, tram operators, technicians, shuttle pilots and crew

Selecting Winners:

Each separate job counts one point toward selecting a "fluency" winner no matter how similar the jobs; but **all** those that fit under one category count as one point for determining the "flexibility" winner. All of a student's answers could fit under only one category, giving only one point for flexibility. At this time, help them see how changing the mind-set or shifting gears to another category may help the students develop many more total solutions on the fluency count also.

There are several ways to select the "elaboration" winner. You could ask each student to select his/her best or most unusual job to explain fully to the class or to draw it using all the details needed to help the class understand it fully. The one with the clearest explanation or most details (showing tools, clothing, etc.) could be declared the "elaboration" winner. Another way is to ask students to select one they have already written to submit as the most detailed or elaborated solution.

There are four categories of winners in creative problem solving: fluency, flexibility, originality, and elaboration.

Problem 7: 3 lab technicians, 6 nurses, 1 doctor, 2 x-ray technicians.
One method: (algebra) The smallest unit is the doctor, so it becomes the unknown quantity from which all others can be determined -
X = doctor, $2X$ = x-ray technician, $3X$ = lab technicians, $6X$ = nurses
Maybe the students can work it this way without actually getting into algebra:
The smallest number of people are the doctors, so we will write them as 1 (meaning we may need to multiply 1 times a number if we need to). The next smallest unit is the x-ray technicians, which is 2 times the number of doctors, so write them as 2. The next smallest unit is the laboratory technicians, which is 3 times the number of doctors, so 3 X 1 = 3 for the lab technicians. The largest group must be the nurses. Since the lab technicians equal 1/2 the nurses, we would write the nurses as 6 (lab technicians [3] times 2 = nurses) so 1 + 2 + 3 + 6 = 12. Each must equal 1 since 12 ÷ 12 = 1.

Challenge: 9 lab technicians, 18 nurses, 3 doctors, and 6 x-ray technicians.
Use the same formula: X = doctor, $2X$ = x-ray technician, $3X$ = lab technicians, $6X$ = nurses. $X + 2X + 3X + 6X = 36$ jobs, so $X = 3$. Another solution: 36 = 3 x 12, multiply each above answer by 3.

Problem 8: No solution slip is provided. Notebook paper or art paper is needed for the solution. Give badges to all students who have equipment and ideas for a variety of activities for adults, children, groups, and individuals with easy movement of equipment for dual use of spaces.

Problem 9: Have students explain and defend their systems to the class. You may give presenters of all good systems a badge, or ask the class to vote on the best five or so systems. Some possibilities for points of reference are: letters, Greek letters, colors, numbers, names (of astronauts, planets, star systems, etc.), Earth landmarks, or cities.

Problem 10: Answers: The Indigo family lives in magenta; the Vermilion family lives in emerald; the Emerald family lives in indigo; and the Magenta family lives in vermilion.

The Indigo family lives only in magenta since they cannot live in the emerald, indigo, or vermilion areas. The Vermilion family does not live in the vermilion or indigo areas, so they must live in magenta or emerald. Since the Vermilion family is opposite the Indigo family, the Indigo family must live in magenta; so the Vermilions live in emerald. Since the Emerald family lives to the right of the Vermilion family, the Emeralds live in indigo. This means the Magenta family lives in vermilion.

Problem 11: Marie should sit in <u>chair 3</u>. The first round of questions sends 2, 4, 6, 8 to the board. The second round sends 1, 5, 9 to the board. The last round sends 7 to the board, leaving 3 alone in the circle.

Problem 12: There are <u>19</u> students in the class. Fill in each section of the circles using the information given in the problem. Add the numbers in each section to reach the total of 18.

Problem 13:
Tommy is in room 142.
Carla is in room 147.
Susie is in room 145.
Mark is in room 143.
Greg is in room 146.
Nicki is in room 144.
The numbers in the grid give the clue used to mark that box. Once a circle is

	142 Mr. George Thompson	143 Dr. Edith Belden	144 Mrs. Ruth Cowen	145 Mrs. Edith Chapman	146 Mrs. Jeri Berrong	147 Dr. Lowell Ensey
Tommy	0	X	X	X	X	X5
Carla	X5	X2	X5	X2	X5	05
Susie	X2	X6	X2	06	X2	X2
Mark	X2	06	X2	X6	X2	X2
Greg	X	X2	X	X2	0	X
Nicki	X4	X2	04	X2	X4	X4

placed showing the correct answer, all boxes in that vertical and horizontal line can have "Xs" placed in them. There is one circle in each horizontal and each vertical line.

Problem 14:
Mrs. McQueen is the business manager.
Mr. Trapani is the editor.
Ms. Moody is the head technician.
Mr. Lee is the reporter.

	Editor	Reporter	Business Manager	Head Technician
Mrs. McQueen	X	X	0	X6
Mr. Trapani	0	X	X1	X1
Ms. Moody	X	X	X	0
Mr. Lee	X2,5	0	X5	X5

Problem 15:
123 words are listed here. There may be more.

Ace, any, ale, asp, an, aye, aces, ales, a, alps, ape, cop, coy, case, can, cane, cap, cape, capes, cool, coal, cope, caps, copes, canes, cans, cops, cone, cones, cools, coop, coops, clean, cleans, clone, clones, clay, clap, claps, colon, lap, loon, lay, leap, lea, lapse, lop, loop, loops, loose, lose, loan, lone, lope, lean, laps, loons, loans, lace, leaps, leans, nay, no, nope, nose, noose, nap, naps, noel, so, spool, spoon, solo, soon, soap, seal, say, sap, son, sop, soy, span, spay, slap, sea, slop, easy, eon, eons, pace, pale, pay, pan, pal, pool, pole, pea, peas, poles, pals, pans, paces, pools, pen, pens, polo, peon, pony, play, plays, plane, planes, peony, on, only, ole, one, yes, yen, yon, yep, yea, yelp.

Problem 16:

1. orbital - adjective
2. yesterday - adverb, noun, adjective
3. insulate - verb
4. scrutinize - verb
5. reuseable - adjective
6. high-speed - adjective
7. flights - noun
8. quickly - adverb
9. payload - noun
10. tomorrow - adverb, noun
11. accelerate - verb
12. flew - verb
13. astronaut - noun
14. technology - noun
15. carefully - adverb

Problem 17:
Review the teacher solution for Problem 6 for more details discussing the solutions. The student giving the most different ways to use a large plastic garbage bag will be named the "fluency" winner.
Anyone naming a way which no else thought of can be named the "originality" winner.
Help the class determine categories for solutions they have heard called out by students. The person with the most categories gets the "flexibility" award. Some categories might be:
1. Containers: luggage, book bag, garbage
2. Wearing apparel: clothing, weave as a belt, overshoes
3. Art: use as a sign, weaving, canvas
4. Shade: block light
5. Protection: book cover, freezer wrap, protect floor from pet, drip cloth
6. Play: tent, doll, hammock, doll clothes, slide for dolls or stuffed toys
7. House accessories: shower curtain

The student with the most detailed or most clearly explained solution gets the "elaboration" award. You could ask each child to choose his/her best or most unusual answer to write, draw, or tell in detail. The class could then choose the winner based on that one answer. You could choose the most detailed from the original lists of students.

Problem 18: Amanda: <u>49</u> + <u>29</u> + <u>55</u> + <u>55</u> + 60 = 248
Christopher: <u>49</u> + <u>49</u> + <u>60</u> + <u>60</u> + 55 = 273
Karon: <u>49</u> + <u>29</u> + <u>60</u> + <u>60</u> + 29 = 227
JoDee: <u>55</u> + <u>60</u> + <u>60</u> + <u>29</u> + 49 = 253

The first step could be to subtract the given information from the total. Then divide by four to estimate the others. Then use the final digit of the total (after subtracting the given number) to estimate if some tosses must end in 5, 0, 9, or multiples of those numbers.

Amanda: 248 - 60 = 188. 188 ÷ 4 = 47 (so two tosses probably above 47 and two tosses below). 188 ends in 8, so two of the tosses must end in 9. Therefore, they would equal the 8 (for 18) final digit, so we will try 49 + 29 = 78. 188 - 78 = 110. 110 ÷ 2 = 55 for the last two numbers.

Christopher: 273 - 55 = 218. 218 ÷ 4 = 54 average (so two tosses above 50 and two below). 218 ends in 8, so two tosses must end in 9. Since the average is over 50, the two below need to be high numbers, so 49 + 49 = 98. 219 - 98 = 120 and 120 ÷ 2 = 60 for the last two numbers.

Karon: 227 - 29 = 198. 198 ÷ 4 = 49 1/2. 198 ends in 8, so two tosses must end in 9 with one higher and one lower, since the average is below 50. 49 + 29 = 78. 198 - 78 = 120. 120 ÷ 2 = 60 for the last two numbers.

JoDee: 253 - 49 = 204. 204 ÷ 4 = 51 average. 204 ends in 4. Two tosses must end in 9 and 5, so they can add up to 14 for a final digit of 4. The 9 number must be 29, since the average is 51, the other numbers are all over 50, and only one of those ends in 5. 29 + 55 = 84. 204 - 84 = 120. 120 ÷ 2 = 60 for the final two tosses.

Problem 19: Accept any answers that fit the definition and description. Some possible answers are:
1. Sun's rays warm the spaceship: heat treat or hot spot
2. Appearances of **Discover** on radar: blip ship
3. Smooth sailing of **Beyond** in orbit: glide ride
4. Sun's appearance from Earth and **Beyond**: bright light or hot spot

1. Light fixture in propulsion area: rocket socket
2. Hard, rock-like appearance of Venus from **Beyond**: granite planet

Problem 20:
1. Moon is to Earth as Titan is to <u>Saturn</u> (moon or satellite to planet).
2. Vostock I is to Yuri Gagarin as Mercury Redstone 3 is to <u>Alan Shephard</u> (space vehicle to first person in space from that country: USSR to USA).
3. Pisces is to fishes as Taurus is to <u>bull</u> (constellation to English name).
4. Telescope is to Hans Lippershay as laser is to <u>Theodore Naiman</u> (invention to inventor: Lippershay - 1648 in Holland: Naiman - 1960 in USA).

Problem 21: Answer: M. Krane and B. Franks because all the samples had last names that had R as its second letter.

Accept any other answer that meets the criteria of all those in the first row having that characteristic and none in the second row having it.

Problem 22: Edra's shortest route is drawn with a dotted line. Julie's shortest route is drawn with a dashed line. Students can use string to measure the distances. <u>Julie</u> lives the shortest route from the library.

Problem 23: LIVING IN SPACE MUST BE FUN

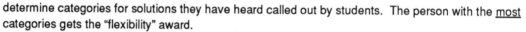

LGIVERING RIN SPFACE
MBUST BEE FSUN

Problem 24: Review the teacher solution for Problem 6 for more details for solution discussion. The student giving the <u>most</u> different ships will be named the "fluency" winner. Anyone naming a way which no one else thought of can be named the "originality" winner. Help the class determine categories for solutions they have heard called out by students. The person with the <u>most</u> categories gets the "flexibility" award.

Some categories might be:
1. Kinds of ships: steamboat, yacht, trawler, liner, whaler, merchant, cruiser, destroyer, aircraft carrier, transport, fishing, clipper, etc.
2. People: shipmate
3. Condition: shipshape, friendship
4. Event: shipwreck
5. Place: shipyard
6. Names of ships: <u>Enterprise, Challenger, Queen Mary,</u> etc.
7. Categories of ships: air, war, sailing

The student with the most detailed or most clearly explained solution gets the "elaboration" award. You could ask each child to choose his/her best or most unusual answer to write, draw, or tell in detail. The class could then choose the winner based on that one answer.

Problem 25:

	Answers	Possible Challenge Answers
Comet:	Halley	Encke, Pons Brooks, Olbers, Faye, Tempel-2
Planet:	Pluto	Mercury, Venus, Earth, Mars, Jupiter, Saturn, Uranus, Neptune
Asteroid:	Ceres	Hermes, Chiron Hidalgo, Icarus
Moon:	Miranda	Phobos, Deimos, Pan, Triton, Mimas, Demeter, Io Europa
Star:	Sun	Sirius, Capella, Betelgeuse, Spica, Deneb, Rigel, Vega
Galaxy:	Milky Way	Large Magellanic Cloud, Ursa Minor system, Draco system
Constellation:	Ursa Major	Andromeda, Aquarius, Cancer, Leo, Orion

Problem 26: Answer: My family will come to live on **Beyond** soon!
Code: Read the first word, skip one word, read the second word, skip two words, read the third word, skip three words, etc., until you leave out eight words and end with soon!

Problem 27: Students should try to determine that the pieces can be divided into small squares. Counting those, they will get 25. Since the area is 25, each side of the big square will equal 5 squares (area = length X width). Accept any arrangement that works.

Problem 28: Things to consider and include: sitting space, area for display, communication methods, storage, information sources (to take the place of textbooks, encyclopedias, etc.), teaching methods, aesthetic considerations.

Problem 29:

1. IN SPACE
2. SPACE PROGRAM
3. ORBITING
4. SUN SPOTS
5. SPACE WALK
6. WEIGHTLESSNESS

Problem 30: The answers are:

```
2 4 6
1 9 5
3 8 7
```

Clue 3:   Row 1 is 2, 4, 6 or 4, 6, 8 in consecutive order.

Clue 4:   Opposite corners must have one low and one high number in each diagonal.

Clue 5:   Row 2 will include numbers 1 and 9 and either 3, 5, or 7 in any order.

Clue 7:   Row 1 must be 2, 4, 6, since 8 is not a factor of 12.

Clue 10: Column 1 must be numbers 1, 2, 3, since we know row 1 starts with 2. Column 3 must be 6, 7, 8 or 5, 6, 7 (but not in counting order), since column 3 starts with 6.

Clue 6:   Since the sum of column 1 equals 6, column 3 must be 3 x 6 or 18. Therefore, column 3 is 6, 5, 7 or 6, 7, 5.

Clue 9:   Since the sums of the diagonals are equal and they share a common center number, the sum of the opposite corners must be equal. Add the possible corners to go with the known corners 2 and 6, so 2 + 5 = 7 or 2 + 7 = 9 and 6 + 1 = 7 or 6 + 3 = 9. The only odd number left for the middle of row 2 is 9 (clue 5).

Clue 4:   The sum of the four corners equals each diagonal, so test 2 + 6 + 7 + 3 = 18 and 2 + 6 + 5 + 1 = 14. Therefore, 7 and 3 are the lower corners to equal 18 (the sum of the diagonals). That leaves row 2 to be 1, 9, 5. Finally, row 3 is 3, 8, 7, since 3 + 8 + 7 =18 (clue 8).

Problem 31:

1. Chicago: space centers
2. Electrodes: primary (natural) energy sources
3. Soyuz: U.S. manned space mission names
4. Richard E. Byrd: astronauts
5. Atlantis: U.S. space shuttles

Problem 32: The letter order for the shortest route is Mars, F (6), E (8), K (3), Earth.
Perhaps the quickest way is to figure each letter separately according to the time it would take. Therefore, each meter of bumpy road is written as 4.

Totals are:
A = 3 1/2 (smooth)
B = 7 (smooth)
C = 16 (bumpy 4 X 4)
D = 2 (smooth)
E = 8 (bumpy 2 X 4)
F = 6 (bumpy 1 1/2 x 4)

G = 3 1/2 (smooth)
H = 9 (smooth)
I = 3 (smooth)
J = 16 (bumpy 4 X 4)
K = 3 (smooth)

Using the above "time" distance, the shortest route equals 17. Other short routes are Mars, F (6), H (9), I (3), Earth = 18
Mars, F (6), J (16), Earth = 22
The route with the longest time is Mars, C (16), D (2), E (8), Venus, J (16), Earth = 42

Problem 33: 1. B   2. E   3. G   4. F   5. D   6. A   7. C   8. H

Problem 34: A Venn Diagram, named after the man who devised it, can be used to determine if conclusions are logical or not. It consists of 3 overlapping circles.

Step 1: Draw a separate circle for each of the 3 categories in your given statements.
Step 2: Have all circles overlap one another. Label each circle.
Step 3: Shade in areas which do not have characteristics or traits in common.
Step 4: Mark an "X" in areas to show the circles have that trait or characteristic in common.
Step 5: Analyze circles and statements.

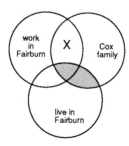

Answer: Number 3

1. Number 1 cannot be true because we shaded where relatives and astronauts overlap, showing no relatives are astronauts.
2. Number 2 may or may not be true, since we have a lot more relatives in the unmarked part of the circle but no statement about pilots who are not astronauts nor a statement about female relatives.
3. Number 3 must be true because we see an unmarked overlapped area between men and astronauts but also a large area of men who are not astronauts.

Problem 35: Answer: Number 2

1. Number 1 may or may not be true since there are other members of the Cox family who do not work at Fairburn Printers. We do not know if they work somewhere else in Fairburn.
2. Number 2 is true since some members of the Cox family do work at Fairburn Printers. There must also be some who do not work there.
3. Number 3 may or may not be true since the overlap circles show there are other people who work in Fairburn at the printers, and we do not know where they live, so they may live in Fairburn.

Challenge: Possibilities: Some people who work in Fairburn do not live there. Some people who live in Fairburn work in Fairburn.

Problem 36: Have students give their speeches to the class. They could tell about food, entertainment, school, work, housing, etc. Honor all students who do well.

Holiday Bonus #1

No answer sheet provided. Provide plain paper for students to sketch their creations. You may display all creations or have students show and explain their work.

Holiday Bonus #2

The letters spell the custom of GIFT SWAP.
The analogy answers are: Letter S = C   Letter W = B or C   Letter A = C   Letter P = C

Holiday Bonus #3

You may want students to create their own hearts or duplicate copies of the solution slip to give them patterns for different size hearts. Let participants choose the category/categories in which they wish to compete.

**Critical Thinking Problem Solving Books
available for grades 1-6:**

JI 2407   Grade 1
JI 2408   Grade 2
JI 2409   Grade 3
JI 2410   Grade 4
JI 2411   Grades 5-6